MW00931363

To the Robson Family

Author: Serena Lane Ferrari (www.serenalaneferrari.com)
Illustrator: Camilla Frescura - Luis Peres
Graphic Designer: Valentina Modica
Published by Green Ventures

ISBN: 978-88-946814-2-0

Serena Lane Ferrari

Our Magical Planet

We Are Earth Protectors

Chapter 1

The secret forest

Sophia and Liam chase each other along the trail into the secret forest.

"Are you sure this is the place mentioned in that book you read?" Liam asks.

"Absolutely!" Sophia nods. "This is the magic path mentioned in the lost pages of the book, *The Hidden Spacehip*. It's brilliant."

"What's so fantastic about it?"

"Because," replies Sophia, blinking her eyes, "it is full of mystery! It says there's something secret and exciting in this exact forest, and now we're here checking it out to see if it's true!"

"I don't really like mystery books. I prefer my science book *The Milky Way*," replies Liam.

"Okay," says Sophia, "tell me what's so good about that book?"

"It explains that on a clear, dark night, you can actually see the Milky Way galaxy. If you look up at the sky when it's dark, arcing overhead will be an irregular luminous band of stars that looks like spilt milk," explains Liam, pointing up towards the sky.

"I like books about mysteries, that sort of thing," frowns Sophia. "Anyway, we'll find out today if the mystery is true. Is there something secret and magical in this forest?"

"At the centre of the Milky Way is one of the creepiest and deadliest things in the universe: The Blackhole," Liam continues, not believing for a minute that Sophia's story could be true.

"What's that?" Sophia cries, grabbing hold of Liam's arm.

Chapter 2

Something unusual

"Look, there! Something is sticking out from behind those trees," Sophia whispers, pointing at the thing. "What is it?"

"I think we should go back home now. It's getting dark and ... it could be dangerous," Liam says uncertainly.

"Are you afraid?" asks Sophia.

"Of course not!" stammers Liam, noticing Sophia is right. There is something unusual-looking behind the trees.

"This could be the secret thing we're supposed to find!" Sophia smiles. "I knew the book was right!"

Holding hands, they shuffle closer to the trees.

A flashing beam of light shines towards them.

Liam's mouth opens wide. "A spaceship!" he exclaims.

As they approach, the spaceship's doors slide open, just like magic.

"Welcome to the flashB12," a tinny-sounding voice says. "Please take your seats!"

The friends first pop their heads in and stare inside the spaceship. There are lots of buttons and controls inside, but they can't see who the voice belongs to.

Liam whispers, "Shall we run away? On my three, let's go back!"

"Liam, there is no back. Look! The path has disappeared ..." says Sophia, searching for the path behind them. It has vanished!

They stare at each other; the only sound is their hearts beating fast.

"I think!" she continues, "this is our adventure!" and into the spaceship she jumps.

Liam isn't so sure, but he follows her in a suspicious manner.

Instantly, the door slides shut. There's a great CLUNK and tremendous noise. A cloud with a terrible smell surrounds them. They both feel dizzy and sleepy ...

CHAPTER 3
The hidden spaceship

The spaceship blasts off into space!

"Sophia! What did you *do*?" demands Liam.

"Me?" Sophia gives Liam a hard stare. "Nothing!"

Before long, the friends are lost in space.

They gaze out at the stars and planets. They are beautiful.

"It's amazing!" murmurs Liam. "Too amazing to be afraid."

The spaceship has flown them beyond the Solar System. They are speeding across the Milky Way galaxy!

"This is scientifically impossible. It can't be true! We must be dreaming!" says Liam. "It looks even more amazing than in my encyclopedia!"

"We must be part of one of the lost pages of the mystery book. But what's happening?" Sophia looks scared.

The spaceship has begun to tremble and shiver and creak.

All of a sudden, it dives into something resembling a blackhole!

The spaceship twists and turns.

It spins and whirls.

"I feel like I'm on a rollercoaster!" Sophia screams.

"I think I'm going to vomit!" says Liam, his face turning green.

CRASH! SMASH! BANG!

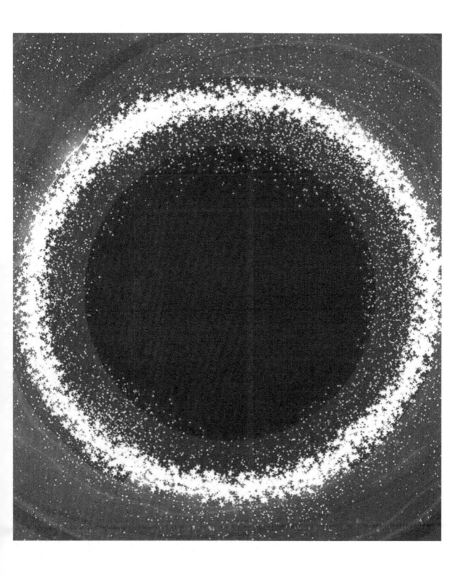

Chapter 4

The magical-looking world

Liam topples over and bumps his bum. "Ow! What's happened? Where are we?"

"I think we've landed," Sophia whispers, "but I don't know where."

The children watch as the door slides back.

"You can now exit the spaceship," says a metallic voice from the control panel.

Liam scrambles to his feet. "Does that mean we should leave?"

"Yes," replies Sophia, "I think it does."

Fearful and puzzled, they walk towards the door.

"Shall we hold hands?" whispers Liam.

"Yes, let's walk out," says Sophia, grabbing his hand.

And together, they step outside.

A magical-looking world surrounds them. There are lush green plants and brightly coloured flowers. Strange alien creatures roam free on the land.

The planet is filled with places between magic and mystery, from natural wonders to caves. Enchanting views leave the children spellbound.

"Hello!" the voice that speaks is fruity and deep. "Welcome! My name is Captain Nature, and this is Planet RC, the rescue centre for lost animals."

CHAPTER 5

Captain alien

Liam gasps as he sees an alien step out of the shadows. "I know you!" he cries. "I've had dreams about you! You're an alien!"

Sophia holds Liam's hand tighter. "I think I have seen him in one of my picture books. He looks like Ualalumpa" she whispers.

"Oh, yes, very friendly," replies Liam.

"Thank goodness for that." Sophia feels relieved.

"Yes, I look like Ualalumpa. This is the shape we have when us aliens show up to you. Although, actually, you are the aliens here!" Captain Nature laughs. "You see, once you open a book and start reading, you are torn into its magic. So I sent the spaceship to collect you and fly you here. I've brought you to our planet to give you a special task."

The alien leads them towards a huge telescope.

"Look through our telescope," he says. "Look at your Planet Earth. It's falling apart. The sea is full of plastic. The rainforests are being destroyed. You have many plants and animals on the brink of extinction. The air is badly polluted. Australia is on fire.

Have you ever seen what happens in intensive farming? Factory farming is fuelling climate change, releasing vast quantities of carbon dioxide and methane. Basically, you are producing too much greenhouse-gas and you are damaging your planet."

"Oh!" says Sophia in shock.

"And you also have nasty viruses brought from animal abuse," the alien adds.

Liams's cheeks go red.

"You are not taking care of your planet," says Captain Nature. His voice is stern. "We have a rescue centre here. We've already saved some of your animals that have all died out on Earth. They can live here. For you, though," he goes on, "for humans, there is no rescue centre, no Planet B."

Chapter 6
Extinct animals

"Let me show you some of the animals we've preserved."

Liam and Sophia follow Captain Nature.

"Here is the Dodo:

It lived in Mauritius till humans showed up.

The dodo went extinct on planet Earth at the end of the 17th century."

"The Great Auk:

It became extinct on planet Earth in the mid-19th century. They were crushed by humans."

"The Quagga:

The quagga were wiped out by hunters in the late 19th century.

It resembles a mixture between a zebra and a horse."

"The Steller's Sea Cow:

Steller's sea cows were captured to extinction in the 18th century."

"Here is my favourite, the Tasmanian Tiger:

The last one on Earth died in a zoo in 1936."

Captain Nature sobs.

"But children like you, from all over the world, are the key to saving your planet and all the species you still have!"

"Us?" Liam and Sophia glimpse at each other. "Really?"

"Yes, with respect for nature! Preserve eco-systems!" the alien states. "Come with me! I also have a gift for you to take home that can help save Planet Earth. This treasure belongs to you. It is buried in a cave, and you must go and find it."

He hands the children a map and two shovels. "These will help you on your quest. But you must be careful! One of the animals there may not be very friendly. Good luck!"

Left alone, the two friends open the map, feeling excited and brave.

How far will they have to walk? How hard will the treasure be to find?

CHAPTER 7

The treasure guardian

Sophia and Liam follow the routes shown on the map. Each one twists and turns and takes them further away from the spaceship.

"I hope we're not lost," says Sophia.

"We must be getting closer," says Liam.

At last, they see the cave.

"There!" Sophia points.

They run, then tip-toe towards the entrance.

Inside, there's no sound, just the dark and the damp.

The map tells them the treasure is hidden where there's an X scratched on the ground. It takes a while for the children's eyes to get used to the dark.

"I see it!" whispers Liam. "I see the X!"

They take the shovels and start to dig.

The ground is hard and heavy, but they scrape and shovel and scoop until finally ...

A treasure chest appears!

"Help me, Sophia!" says Liam.

Together, they manage to pull the chest out.

But before they can open the lid, there's a noise. It comes from deep inside the cave.

"W-w-what was that?" Sophia stammers.

The noise comes again: A terrible trumpeting! It's getting closer!

Through the darkness, two yellow eyes glitter ...

Two enormous, curved tusks shine brightly in the gloom.

CHAPTER 8

The woolly mammoth

"AAAAAAHHH! It's a monster!" Sophia screams.

"It's a woolly mammoth!" shouts Liam. "That must be the animal Captain Nature warned us about!"

Carrying the treasure chest between them, they turn and scramble out of the cave.

They run past the extinct animals, ...

... past Captain Nature, "Hey kids, don't run so fast, he won't harm you!" he shouted, ...

... back through the magical-looking world around them, ...

... and, finally, to the spaceship.

"Can you see the mammoth?" cries Liam.

Sophia shakes her head. Luckily, they seem to have left it behind.

Breathless, Liam and Sophia heave the chest into the spaceship and step aboard.

Together they open the chest.

CHAPTER 9
The letter

Inside, they find a sealed letter. There are instructions written on it:

- Reuse and recycle

- Use less plastic and ditch single-use plastics

- Use reusable water bottles

- Avoid products containing microbeads

- Use reusable shopping bags

- Participate in a beach or river clean-up

- Eat less meat

- Plant a vegetable garden and eat fruits and vegetables that are grown near your home

- Walk or use bicycles to get around instead of cars

- Turn off the water when you're brushing your teeth

- Save electricity

"If every person does something – even if it's very small – together, you can help save the planet," Sophia reads.

There is also an envelope inside the chest. It's full of lots of different kinds of seeds and seedlings to plant.

"A mature leafy tree can produce enough oxygen for ten people over a year," echoes Captain Natures's disembodied voice.

"Where are you?" asks Liam

"I'm everywhere but invisible," replies Captain Nature's voice. "It's time for you to go home and help other children understand their importance."

"I'm sleepy," yawns Sophia as the dark settles all around.

Sophia and Liam look upwards through the spaceship's windows. They admire the moons that gleam above them. They relax and stare at the night. Feeling tired, they fall asleep.

CHAPTER 10

The dream

A thunderstorm wakes them.

Rain drip-drops onto their faces.

The children find themselves lying on the trail in the secret forest, right back where their adventure began.

"We must have fallen asleep," says Sophia, sitting up. "I think I had a dream about finding the secret thing in the forest that was mentioned in my book."

Liam nods, jumping to his feet. "I think I had a dream, too."

But when they glance down, they see something …

The letter and seeds are still clasped in their fingers!

"Keep seeing the magic in ordinary things!" Liam reads from the seed packet. "We know what we have to do, Sophia. Come on! Let's plant these seeds, follow the instructions from the chest, and help spread the word about making changes, so we can all save the planet!"

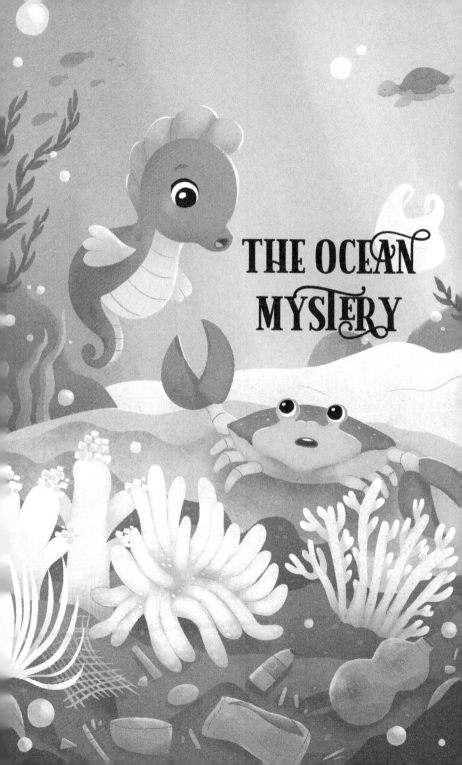

THE OCEAN
MYSTERY

CHAPTER 1

Tabatha's enchanting world

Tabatha was a kind little seahorse. She was always happy and was always giggling.

Tabatha loved to swim. Sometimes, she even pretended to be a mermaid. She would whirl and twirl through the swaying green seaweed, smiling and giggling.

One day, Tabatha's mother said, "Tabatha, now that you're growing up, I think the time has come for you to go out and explore the ocean on your own. You can swim and dance all day, if you like. But remember, you must come back home before it's dark."

"Oh, thank you, thank you, thank you!" Tabatha cried. She bobbed her pudgy head up and down. "I feel like a grown-up already! Can I go now? Can I explore the Great Barrier Reef?"

"Yes, my sweetheart, I haven't been for a long time, but it is beautiful, so colourful! But you must be careful, Tabatha. Don't go as far as the Plastic Ocean!"

Tabatha looked puzzled. "What's the Plastic Ocean, Mama?" she asked.

Tabatha's mother looked sad. "It's a very large part of the ocean," she said, "a part that's filled with piles of plastic bottles and bags and other plastic junk that the humans have left behind. It is the most dangerous place to be. If you see it up ahead, be sure to turn back right away!"

"OK, Mama!" shouted Tabatha, and she swam away in a flash as fast as a sailfish.

Tabatha was excited. She began to dive and dance like a ballerina, popping in and out of the water like a dolphin.

Her curiosity always led her towards magical adventures, and now she was ready to explore!

40

CHAPTER 2

Tabatha's adventure

Tabatha swam past a family of crabs sitting on the rocks. They waved at her as she sailed by.

"Tabathaaaaa! It's me! Lionel!"

A giant crab started to chase Tabatha, snapping his mighty claws.

"Lionel!" Tabatha said. "I'm so happy to see you! Would you like to join my adventure? I'm going to look at the Great Barrier Reef!"

Lionel didn't need asking twice. "I'm in!" he said.

Tabatha had once saved Lionel from a fisherman's trap. The trap had been hidden, but Tabatha had discovered it just in time. They soon became best friends, played together, and had a secret adventure club. Sometimes, they would swim and dance with other strange creatures in the great Pacific Ocean.

They glided beside a huge whale shark who was very gentle and kind.

They pirouetted with a dugong and sang with Tally, the Sea Turtle.

They played bump with sponges.

At last, they were in the Great Barrier Reef, home to some of the most incredible creatures on the planet. What an amazing place to be!

Tabatha let the current carry her along.

"Whoa!" said Lionel, swimming by what just looked like an ordinary white rock. "Why are the colours missing? What's happened to the bright corals?"

Tabatha looked around her. "I can't believe this," she said. "Someone has stolen the colours!"

Chapter 3

The missing colours

"I think it's the snow witch, the one from the book we read," said Lionel.

"Don't be silly!" Tabatha replied. "That's just a made-up story." She frowned. Then an idea popped into her head. "Let's go and ask Wise Octopus! He'll know where the colours have gone." Tabatha swam off swiftly. "Come on, Lionel! Chop, chop!"

Lionel nodded happily and followed Tabatha. He had lots of legs, so it was easy for him to keep up.

They found Wise Octopus. He was swaying his eight long tentacles like a drummer. Wise Octopus was working hard to create the perfect den for himself and was the best at camouflage.

"Wise Octopus," said Tabatha, "could you please tell us why the coral reef is turning white? There can't be snow in the ocean!"

Wise Octopus stared at the two of them. He could be grumpy sometimes, but he was the cleverest creature of all.

"Hmm ...," Wise Octopus began, "when water is too warm, corals push out the algae that live in them. The algae are actually called zooxanthellae. You say it like this: **zoo-zan-thell-ay**. It's what gives coral its colour. So, when the algae get pushed out, the coral turns completely white. This is called 'coral bleaching'."

"Oh no! What can we do to get the colours back?" asked Tabatha. "I think the corals are suffering."

"They certainly are suffering!" Octopus snapped. "But I'm afraid you can't help. It has to come from there," Octopus pointed upwards with one tentacle.

"Where?" asked Lionel.

"From outside the ocean," Octopus replied. "From those funny creatures called humans.

44

The main reason for coral bleaching is climate change, the planet warming up. A warm planet means a warm ocean. If the temperature rises by as little as 1-2 degrees Celsius, corals can turn white. But please," Octopus yawned sleepily, "now it's my nap time. Come back tomorrow to learn more."

Tabatha and Lionel felt sad, but they were curious to return the next day and learn more.

Chapter 4

The dangerous way

Together, Tabatha and Lionel went gliding and sliding for miles. There was so much to discover in the ocean: Creatures Tabatha and Lionel had never seen before.

There were yellow fish with black stripes. There were bright pink fish with blue tails. There was even one fish that looked like a glowing blue light.

Soon, Tabatha and Lionel saw a patch of lovely bright colours that seemed to float among the rocks. Strange shapes bounced up and down in the water. Some came to rest on the ocean floor.

Tabatha had never seen anything like it. Being a curious little seahorse, she swam closer.

Lionel swam closer, too. Then: "NO!" he screamed. He suddenly realised what they were looking at. "IT'S THE PLASTIC OCEAN!"

As quickly as he could, he turned round and scuttled off to hide in a nearby cave. "Hurry, Tabatha!" he yelled. "Swim away as fast as you can! Come, hide with me!"

But it was too late.

Poor Tabatha had got too close. She was already trapped inside a plastic bottle!

She tried to escape. She looped and curled. She spun and jumped. But she couldn't find the way out.

"SAVE ME! SAVE ME, LIONEL!" she cried. "I'M STUCK IN A PLASTIC BOT-TLE!"

Lionel was scared, so scared, he could hardly think. What should he do? He didn't want to swim any closer, but he had to save his friend!

48

CHAPTER 5

Friendship

"I'M COMING, TABATHA!" Lionel hollered. "I'M COMING!"

Quick as a wink, Lionel flung himself towards Tabatha. He raised his big, powerful claws and snapped open the bottle she was trapped inside. Then, he squeezed the end with all his strength. Out Tabatha flew, rolling over and over in the water.

Tabatha felt so dizzy, she almost couldn't swim. She clung to Lionel with her tail, and together, the two friends made their escape.

When they were well away from the Plastic Ocean, Tabatha said, "Thank you, my dear friend, for saving me! We've made it out safely, but other fish might not be so lucky. From now on, let's tell everyone we know how dangerous it is to throw plastic into our ocean! We have to find a way to let humans know that they're putting us at risk! If it wasn't for your big claws, you'd never have been able to save me!"

"You're right," said Lionel. "Let's make signs to tell everyone not to throw plastic into the ocean! We want the ocean to be safe, so all of us – even the humans – can enjoy it. We should tell them they're warming up the ocean too, and it's making the corals turn white! Should we say anything else?"

"Let's go back to Wise Octopus tomorrow!" Tabatha suggested. "He'll tell us what to do."

"Yes, great idea!" replied Lionel. "He didn't finish telling us about coral bleaching, and I want to know more. The more we know, the more we can do to help stop it."

"Yes!" agreed Tabatha. "The more we know, the more we can do to help save the ocean!"

The next day, Tabatha, Lionel, and Wise Octopus made signs to teach humans important ways they can help save the oceans.

WISE OCTOPUS'S TIPS TO HELP SAVE THE OCEANS:

- Don't use chemicals in sinks or gutters. Make sure all your bath products are environmentally friendly

- Try not to let rubbish wash down drains – it could end up in the ocean

- Use re-usable shopping bags rather than plastic bags

- When you're out and about, always take your rubbish home with you

- Don't start a live-rock aquarium. Although live rock is still harvested legally in some places, collecting it causes lots of damage to the reef organisms' habitat

- If you're in a boat, please don't anchor on the reef

- If you dive, don't touch anything, only take pictures and just leave bubbles

- Volunteer to help out! There are very important volunteer and community coral reef monitoring programmes. If you don't live near the sea, get involved in your local "save the river" (or bay, lake, or another estuarine environment) programme

- Use reef-friendly sun protection cream
- Don't use crop fertilisers in your garden

I'm on a mission to **engage children and teenagers** in sustainability. My stories are optimistic and entertaining, sprinkled with magic, friendship, and mystery. I talk about climate change, pollution and environmental issues in a **simple but inspiring style**.

It's never too early to **change the world**, and my books want to **make it fun**.

I love hearing from readers, and welcome you to **interact with me** on instagram (www.instagram.com/serenalaneferrari) or to **contact me** at serenalaneferrari@gmail.com

Would you mind taking a few seconds to leave a review of my book? It's important because **your opinion** helps people make better decisions.

Thank you!

We proudly support

Reforestation is the most
effective method to fight climate change

You buy books, we plant trees.

Venture deep
into the rainforest
with Jingo
and his brave friends

Raise children to love and
respect nature with
Save the Planet Book Series

JINGO the orangutan loves his beautiful jungle habitat — but when bulldozers arrive, can he and his animal friends band together to save their home?

Venture deep into the rainforest with this vividly illustrated picture book!

Parents will enjoy an engaging story that speaks directly to kids showing what **deforestation** can do on animals and wildlife habitats.

Children will love reading about Jingo and his brave friends!

Jingo in the Jungle is based on **the true story** of an orangutan - in Indonesia - defending its home and habitat from being destroyed by a bulldozer.

Follow **Nelson and his friends** in this underwater adventure

Raise children to love and respect nature with **Save the Planet** Book Series

Nelson, once the clumsiest seal in the sea, is always needing his friends to get him out of trouble. When his friends are trapped, can Nelson find **bravery inside** himself and save the day?

Follow his journey in this modern fairytale to find out.

Poor **Clumsy Nelson**, he's always stumbling, bumping or crashing in the plastic polluted sea. We all have times where we feel uncomfortable about who we are. Being clumsy isn't always easy.

Clumsy Nelson is a message of **positive self-esteem, courage, perseverance, and friendship** for any child who has trouble finding the hero inside.

Clumsy Nelson is also a fun and engaging adventure into **environmental awareness**, published by Save the Planet Books.

A story that inspires kids of all ages to **never give up** and empowers **them to find the hero inside.**

According to **United Nations Educational, Scientific and Cultural Organization (UNESCO)**, there are four reasons to provide children with environmental education:

To make them more aware and conscious of environmental problems.

To boost their interest in caring for and improving the environment.

To enhance their ability to learn about their surroundings.

To broaden their ecological knowledge in subjects such as landscapes, air, water, natural resources and wildlife.

Made in the USA
Middletown, DE
11 October 2022